POCKET FUN

TRAVEL
Activity
Book

ARCTURUS

ARCTURUS

This edition published in 2019 by Arcturus Publishing Limited
26/27 Bickels Yard, 151–153 Bermondsey Street,
London SE1 3HA

Illustrated by: Collaborate, Amanda Enright, Genie Espinosa,
Jo Moon, and Leo Trinidad
Designed by: Duck Egg Blue

ISBN: 978-1-78888-731-1
CH006914NT
Supplier 29, Date 0319, Print run 8001

Printed in China

LONDON SiGHTS

London is the capital of the United Kingdom.
Join the dots and hop on the tour bus!

LOST LUGGAGE

This poor pup is lost in the airport baggage claim. Find a way over the conveyor to rescue him, without bumping into any cases.

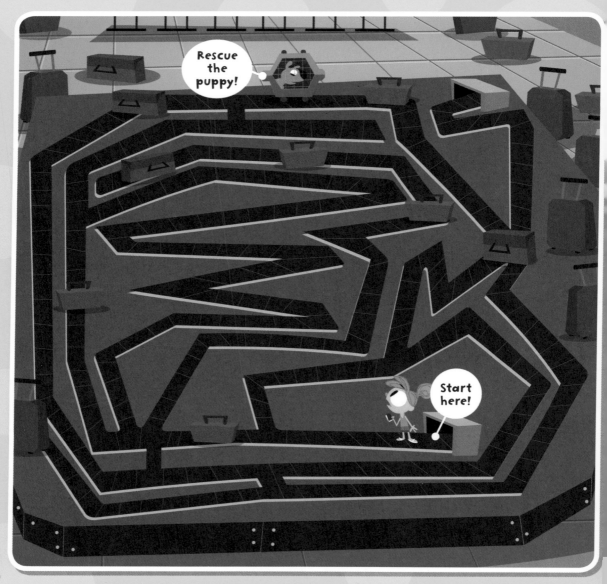

Use the guide below to complete this ballooning scene.

5

DRAW A PLANE

Use the grid lines to help you copy the picture into the blank space.

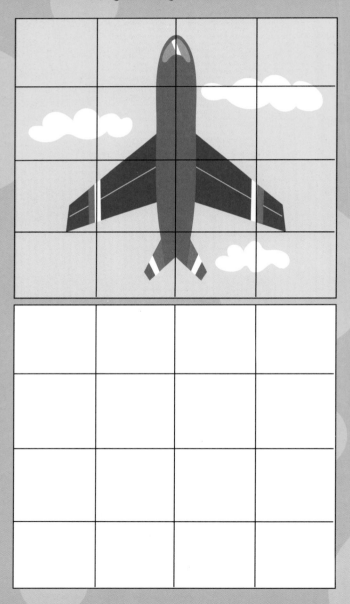

GREAT WALL OF CHINA

This awesome structure is more than 2,000 years old.
Join the dots and take a tour!

Use the guide below to complete this desert scene.

8

AVALANCHE!

Help the skier race away from the avalanche to the rescue plane,
without being clawed by grouchy grizzlies.

TIP TOP TOPPINGS

Can you find a slice in Pablo's pizza that matches the one below?

Find this slice!

TAJ MAHAL

Join the dots to reveal this magnificent Indian white marble building!

SAHARA DESERT

The Sahara is the world's largest hot desert.
Join the dots to discover an animal that lives there!

Complete this fun scene using the guide below.

13

ALL ABOARD!

Quick! This train is just about to leave the station!
Can you spot ten differences between the scenes
below, before the train departs?

UP, UP, AND AWAY!

Join the dots and launch these people on a special sightseeing trip!

Complete the picture using the guide below.

17

UNDERWATER RESCUE

Swim through the octopus arms to free the desperate diver caught on the seabed, and then guide him toward the surface.

AFRICAN GRASSLANDS

Which large animal is enjoying a drink
at the watering hole?

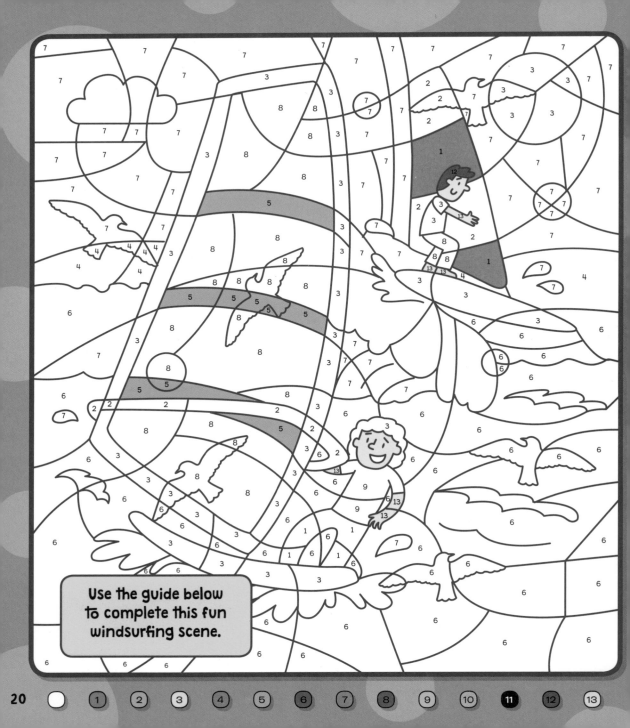

Use the guide below to complete this fun windsurfing scene.

1 2 3 4 5 6 7 8 9 10 11 12 13

ARCTIC ANTICS

Brrrr! Chill out by spotting ten differences below.

EGYPT

Discover some famous old monuments by joining the dots!

Complete the scene using the guide below.

23

AMAZING AQUARIUM

Dive in and see if you can spot ten differences between these busy sea creature scenes.

Use the guide below to complete this Wild West scene.

26 ◯ ① ② ③ ④ ⑤ ⑥ ⑦ ⑧ ⑨ ⑩ ⑪ ⑫ ⑬

CORAL CREATURES

Help the pink fish swim along the lines of coral to find its friends.

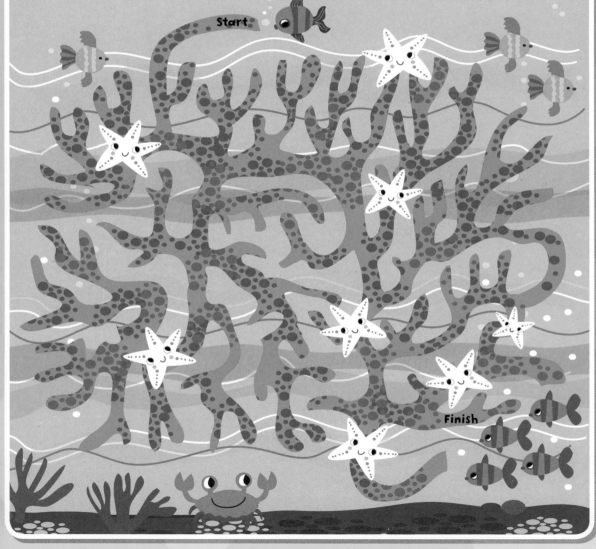

Start

Finish

SAFARI SPOTTING

Join the dots and discover a beautiful creature prowling the plains.

Complete this New York scene using the guide below.

PLANE SPOTTING

Check in and find ten differences before takeoff!

MOUNT FUJI

Join the dots to discover a traditional Japanese sport.

Complete the scene using the guide below.

32

EGYPTIAN ESCAPE

Two tomb trackers have found the pharaoh's treasure. Help them reach it, and escape by dodging mad mummies and scary scarabs.

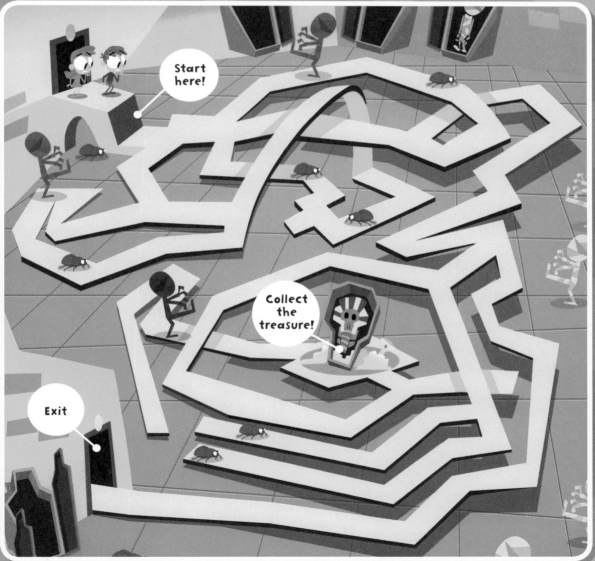

CARNIVAL TIME!

Discover how the people of Rio de Janeiro, in Brazil, like to celebrate!

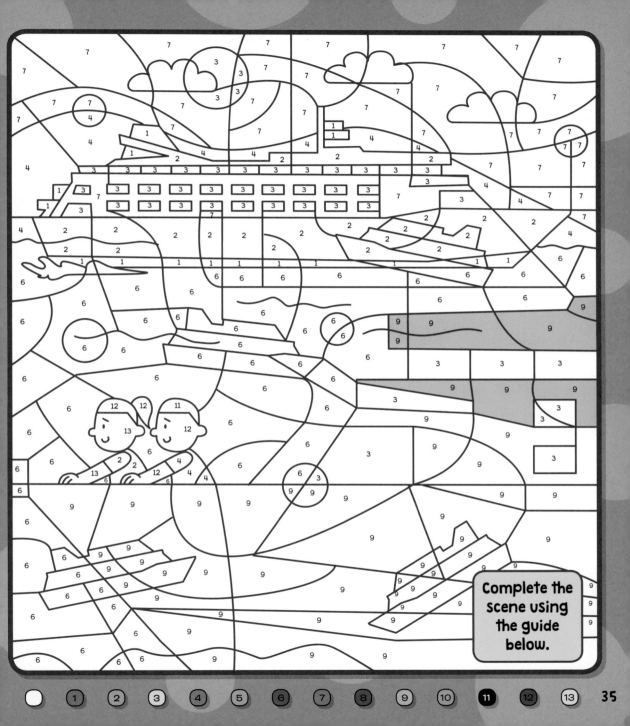

Complete the scene using the guide below.

35

ON THE BEACH

How many sandcastles has Bobby built?
Look at the shape of his bucket.

GLADIATOR SCHOOL

Travel back in time to spot ten differences in Ancient Rome.

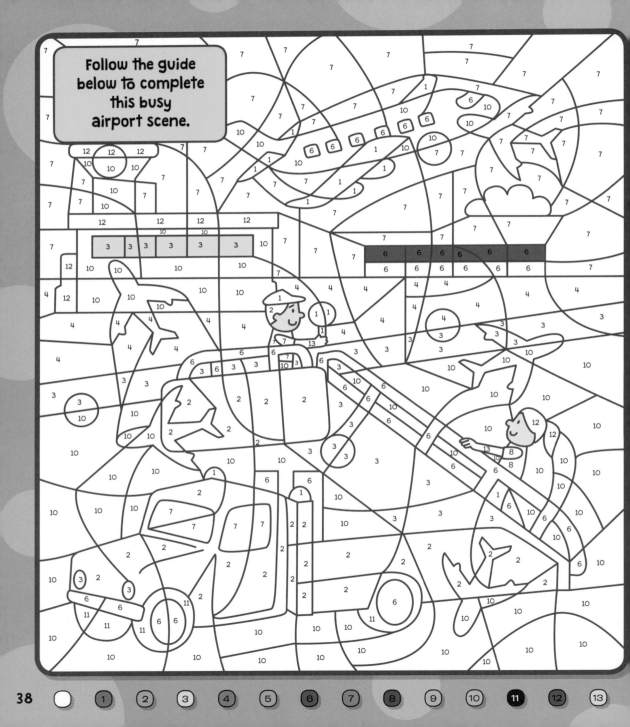

Follow the guide below to complete this busy airport scene.

38

STONEHENGE

Stonehenge in England is one of the world's most famous ancient monuments. Discover it by joining the dots!

SUPER SPLASH!

Are you ready to make a big splash?
Find ten differences between these fun water park scenes.

FROSTY FRIGHTS

Two Arctic explorers need help crossing the sea ice to the research station.
Watch out for the polar bears!

Use the guide below to complete the scene.

43

ROME

Outside which famous monument are these tourists enjoying a refreshing drink? Join the dots to find out!

DRAW A SHARK

Use the grid lines to help you copy the picture into the blank space.

TEMPLE TRAP

To escape the temple maze, the adventurer will have to climb up the rope.
Guide the way, watching out for bad-tempered birds and tumbling rocks.

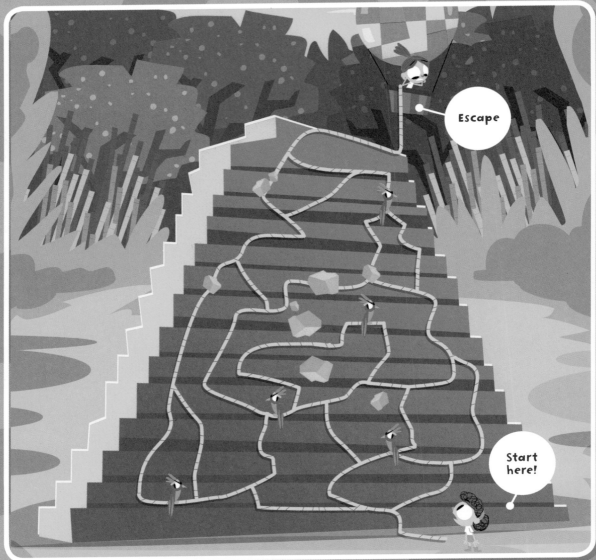

Use the guide below to complete this chilly scene.

47

IN THE ARCTIC

Creatures that live in the snow and ice are often white, so they can hide away. What animals can you spot in this snowy scene?

DOLLS INSIDE DOLLS

Matryoshka are traditional Russian dolls that fit inside each other.
Join the dots to see the set in the shop window.

Complete this Dutch city scene using the guide below.

50

POOL PUZZLE

Splish, splash, and spot ten differences at the pool.

RIO DE JANEIRO

Join the dots to discover a famous statue towering over this Brazilian city.

SWiM TO SHORE

The swim to the beach is full of peril. Find a safe route without touching rocks, spiky urchins, or snappy crabs.

Start here!

Escape

Complete the picture using the guide below.

54

FUN IN THE SUN

Make a splash at the beach and spot ten differences.

ON SAFARI

There are lots of animals to spot on safari,
but can you spot ten differences, too?

SOUTH POLE

Join the dots to see some playful penguins having lots of fun!

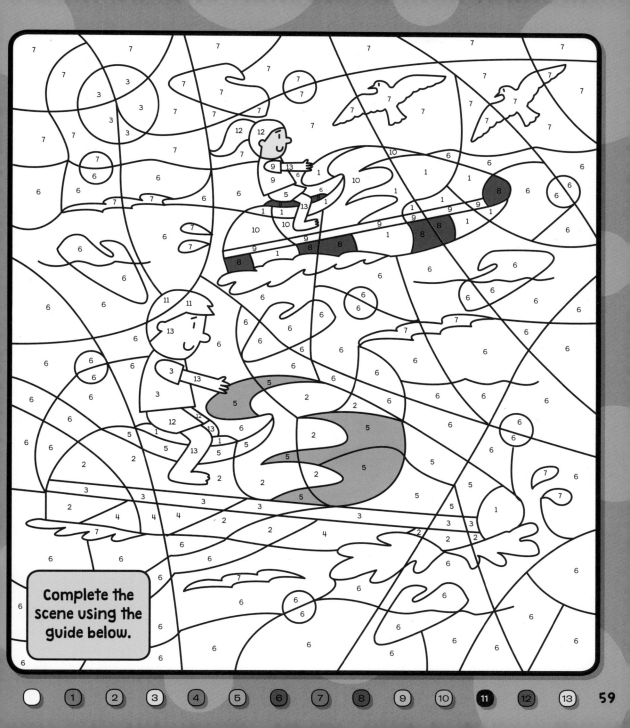

Complete the scene using the guide below.

1 2 3 4 5 6 7 8 9 10 11 12 13   59

DASH IN VENICE

This boy has gelato for his friend. Lead him past the carnival-goers, before it melts!

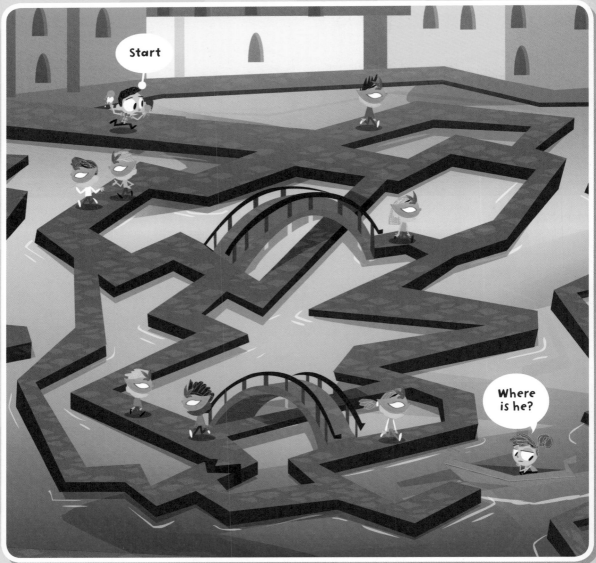

SUNNY DAYS

How many circles can you find in this picture?

Use the guide below to complete this countryside scene.

62

MARCHING ON!

One, two! One, two! Make sure the Queen's Guard keeps up the pace by joining the dots!

CORAL REEF

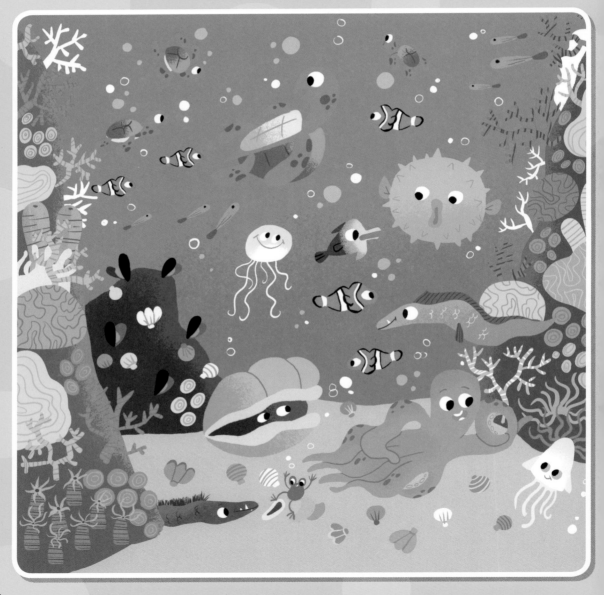

Dive into the sea and explore the coral reef.
Can you find ten differences here below the waves?

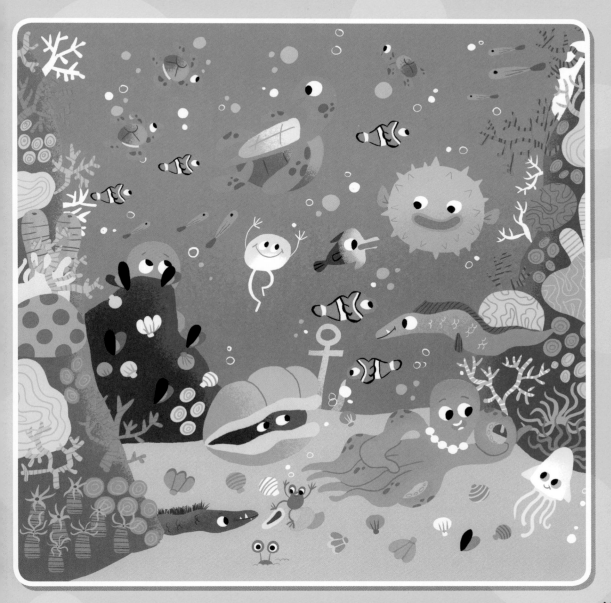

ANGKOR WAT

Discover this beautiful Cambodian temple by joining the dots.

Complete this busy London scene using the guide below.

RAGING RAPIDS

It's a rough ride through the rapids! Lead the boat to safety by dodging the anacondas and piranhas.

MERRY MOSCOW

Join the dots and watch a traditional Russian jig!

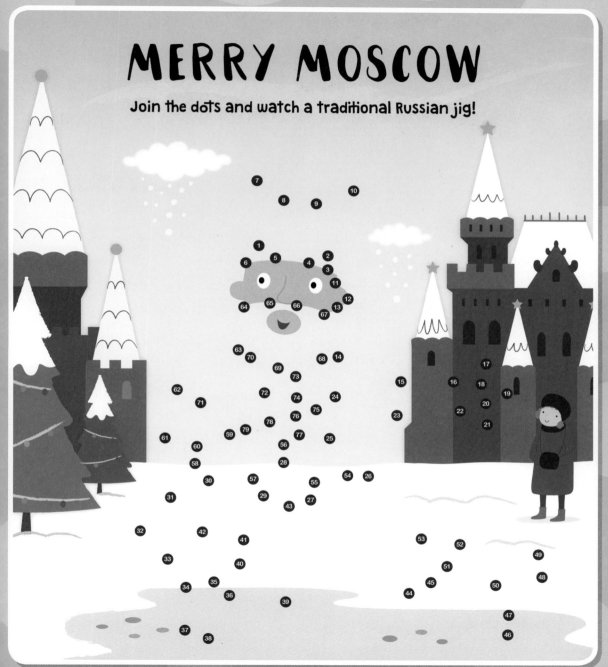

Complete the scene using the guide below.

DESERT TOUR

Can you spot ten differences across the desert sands?

ARC DE TRIOMPHE

Join the dots and marvel at this famous Parisian arch!

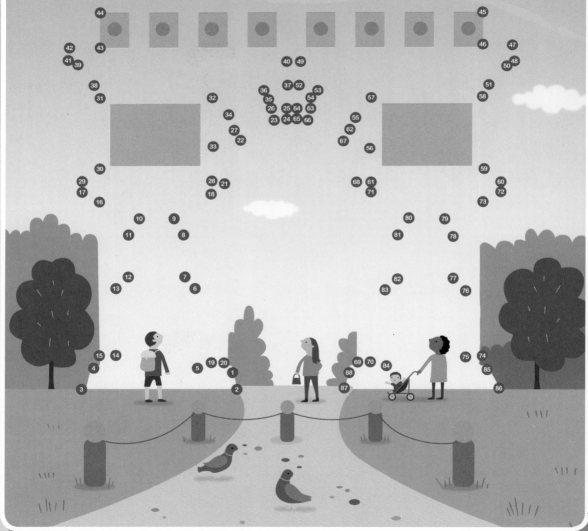

Complete the scene using the guide below.

73

HAPPY NEW YEAR!

It's party time! Can you spot ten differences between these Chinese New Year scenes?

IT'S FIESTA TIME!

What instrument is this Spanish musician playing?

CRESTING THE WAVES

This surfer is riding a huge wave. Help him reach the shore in one piece by following the path, and avoiding surfing turtles.

Complete this Venice scene using the guide below.

WHAT A VIEW!

The Empire State Building is a famous skyscraper in Manhattan, New York.

TiME FOR TEA

Spot ten differences between these Japanese tea party scenes.

Complete this fun snowy scene using the guide below.

81

SING IT LOUD!

Join the dots to discover which famous Australian
"house" this man is singing outside!

MEET THE MINOTAUR

Lead the Greek hero through the maze to fight the
monstrous Minotaur and end his reign of terror.

84

PIÑATA FUN!

Mexican children play with paper piñatas and win lots of sweet treats!

IN THE OUTBACK

Join the dots to reveal a cute and cuddly marsupial, native to Australia.

FLYING HIGH

Search the sky for ten differences between these scenes.

ANSWERS

Page 3 LONDON SIGHTS

Page 7 GREAT WALL OF CHINA

Page 10 TIP TOP TOPPINGS

Page 4 LOST LUGGAGE

Page 8

Page 11 TAJ MAHAL

Page 5

Page 9 AVALANCHE!

Page 12 SAHARA DESERT

Page 13

Page 17

Page 20

Page 14–15 ALL ABOARD!

Page 18 UNDERWATER RESCUE

Page 21 ARCTIC ANTICS

Page 22 EGYPT

Page 16 UP, UP, AND AWAY!

Page 19 AFRICAN GRASSLANDS

Page 23

Page 27 CORAL CREATURES

Page 30 PLANE SPOTTING

Page 31 MOUNT FUJI

Page 24-25 AMAZING AQUARIUM

Page 28 SAFARI SPOTTING

Page 26

Page 29

Page 32

Page 33 EGYPTIAN ESCAPE

Page 34 CARNIVAL TIME!

Page 35

Page 36 ON THE BEACH
Bobby has built 3 sandcastles

Page 37 GLADIATOR SCHOOL

Page 38

Page 39 STONEHENGE

Page 40-41 SUPER SPLASH

Page 42 FROSTY FRIGHTS

Page 43

Page 47

Page 50

Page 44 ROME

Page 48 IN THE ARCTIC

Page 51 POOL PUZZLE

Page 52 RIO DE JANEIRO

Page 49 DOLLS WITHIN DOLLS

Page 46 TEMPLE TRAP

Page 53 SWIM TO SHORE

Page 56–57 ON SAFARI

Page 60 DASH IN VENICE

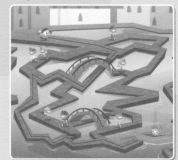

Page 54

Page 58 SOUTH POLE

Page 61 SUNNY DAYS
There are 10 circles in the picture, or 15 if you counted the children's eyes!

Page 62

Page 55 FUN IN THE SUN

Page 59

Page 63 MARCHING ON!

Page 67

Page 70

Page 64–65 CORAL REEF

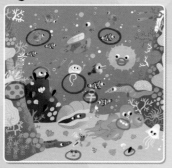

Page 68 RAGING RAPIDS

Page 71 DESERT TOUR

Page 72 ARC DE TRIOMPHE

Page 66 ANGKOR WAT

Page 69 MERRY MOSCOW

Page 73

Page 77 CRESTING THE WAVES

Page 80 TIME FOR TEA

Page 81

Page 74–75 HAPPY NEW YEAR!

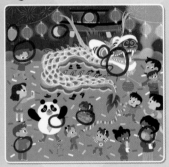

Page 78

Page 82 SING IT LOUD!

Page 76 IT'S FIESTA TIME!

Page 79 WHAT A VIEW!

Page 83 MEET THE MINOTAUR

Page 86 IN THE OUTBACK

Page 84

Page 87 FLYING HIGH

Page 85 PIÑATA FUN!

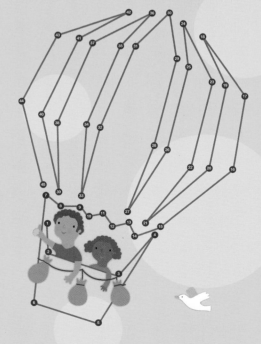